playBASSwith...
20 CLASSIC SONGS

C000143560

Wise Publications
part of The Music Sales Group
London / New York / Paris / Sydney / Copenhagen / Berlin / Madrid / Hong Kong / Tokyo

Published by
Wise Publications
14-15 Berners Street, London W1T 3LJ, UK.

Exclusive Distributors:
Music Sales Limited
Distribution Centre, Newmarket Road,
Bury St Edmunds, Suffolk IP33 3YB, UK.

Music Sales Pty Limited
Units 3-4, 17 Willfox Street,
Condell Park, NSW 2200, Australia.

Order No. AM1006610
ISBN 978-1-78305-123-6
This book © Copyright 2013 Wise Publications,
a division of Music Sales Limited.

Printed in the EU.

www.musicsales.com

Edited by Adrian Hopkins.
Cover designed by Tim Field.
Photo by Tim Mosenfelder/Getty Images.
Photo research by Jacqui Black.
Music engraved by Paul Ewers Music Design.

Your Guarantee of Quality:

As publishers, we strive to produce every
book to the highest commercial standards.
The music has been freshly engraved and the
book has been carefully designed to minimise
awkward page turns and to make playing
from it a real pleasure.
Particular care has been given to specifying
acid-free, neutral-sized paper made from pulps
which have not been elemental chlorine bleached.
This pulp is from farmed sustainable forests
and was produced with special regard for the
environment.
Throughout, the printing and binding have been
planned to ensure a sturdy, attractive publication
which should give years of enjoyment.
If your copy fails to meet our high standards,
please inform us and we will gladly replace it.

Ace Of Spades
For Whom The Bell Tolls
My Generation
Rope
Guitars: Arthur Dick
Bass: Paul Townsend
Drums: Noam Lederman

All Right Now
Brown Eyed Girl
Hey Joe
My Sharona
Livin' On A Prayer
Sweet Home Alabama
Guitars and Bass guitar: Tom Fleming
Drums: Dave Cottrell

I Shot the Sheriff
Guitars: Arthur Dick
Bass Guitar: Paul Townsend
Drums: Noam Lederman
Keyboards: Paul Honey
Percussion: Fergus Gerrand

Lady Madonna
Guitars: Arthur Dick
Bass: Paul Townsend
Drums: Brett Morgan
Saxophone: Howard McGill
Keyboards: Paul Honey

Late In The Evening
Guitars: Arthur Dick
Bass: Paul Townsend
Drums: Noam Lederman
Sax/Trumpet/Trombone: The Fullfat Horns

London Calling
Wonderwall
Guitars: Arthur Dick
Bass: Paul Townsend
Drums: Brett Morgan

Rebel Rebel
Roxanne
Guitars: Arthur Dick
Bass: Paul Townsend
Drums: Ian Thomas

Underground
Keyboards: Paul Honey
Bass: Phil Mulford
Drums: Chris Baron

Voulez-vous
Guitars: Arthur Dick
Keyboards: Paul Honey
Bass: Don Richardson
Drums: Chris Baron

You Shook Me All Night Long
Guitars: Arthur Dick
Bass: Tom Farncombe
Drums: Noam Lederman

BASS GUITAR
TABLATURE EXPLAINED

Bass Tablature *is a four-line staff that graphically represents the bass fingerboard. By placing a number on the appropriate line, the string and fret of any note can be indicated. The number 0 represents an open string. For example:*

3rd string, 3rd fret   4th string, open

SLIDE (not restruck): *Strike the first note and then slide the same fret-hand finger up or down to the second note.*

SLIDE (with restrike): *Same as previous slide, except the second note is struck.*

SLIDE: *Slide up to the note indicated from a few notes below.*

SLIDE: *Strike the note indicated and slide up an indefinite number of frets.*

HAMMER-ON: *Strike the first (lower) note with one finger, then sound the higher note (on the same string) with another finger by fretting it without picking.*

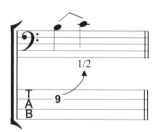

PULL-OFF: *Place both fingers on the notes to be sounded. Strike the first note and without picking, pull the finger off to sound the second lower note.*

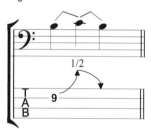

PALM-MUTE: *The note is partially muted by the pick hand lightly touching the string(s) just before the bridge.*

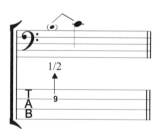

MUFFLED-STRINGS: *A percussive sound is produced by laying the left hand across the string(s) without depressing it to the fretboard.*

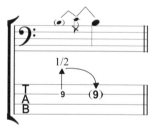

BEND (half step): *Strike the note and bend up a semi-tone (half step).*

BEND & RELEASE: *Strike the note and bend up as indicated, then release back to the original note.*

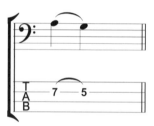

PRE-BEND: *Bend the note as indicated then strike it.*

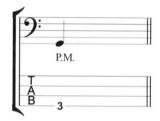

PRE-BEND & RELEASE: *Bend the note as indicated. Strike it and release the note back to the original pitch.*

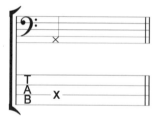

TRILLS: *Very rapidly alternate between the notes indicated by continuously hammering on and pulling off.*

VIBRATO: *The string is vibrated by rapidly bending and releasing the note with the fretting hand.*

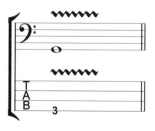

NATURAL HARMONIC: *Strike the note while the fret-hand lightly touches the string directly over the fret indicated.*

TREMOLO PICKING: *The note is picked as rapidly and continuously as possible.*

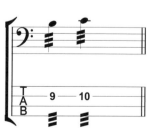

NOTE: *The speed of any bend is indicated by the music notation and tempo.*

ACE OF SPADES

Words and Music by
Ian Kilmister, Eddie Clarke & Phil Taylor

Full performance demo: CD 1, track 1
Backing only: CD 2, track 1

To match recording, tune down a semitone
Intro
1 bar count in:

♩ = 141

N.C.

f w/pick + dist.

(E⁵)

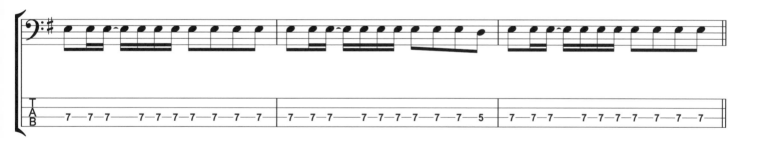

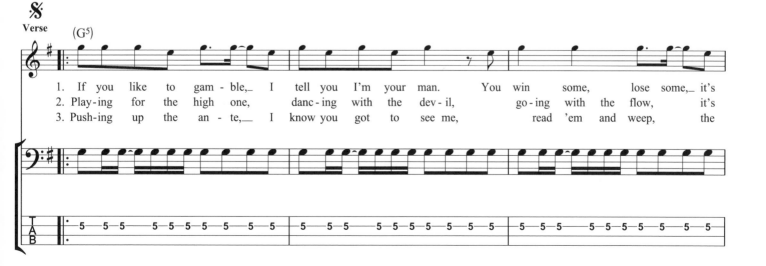

Verse

(G⁵)

1. If you like to gam-ble,__ I tell you I'm your man. You win some, lose some,__ it's
2. Play-ing for the high one, danc-ing with the dev-il, go-ing with the flow, it's
3. Push-ing up the an-te,__ I know you got to see me, read 'em and weep, the

E⁵

D.S. al Coda

Coda

(E⁵)

D⁵/A   C⁵/G

D⁵/A   C⁵/G   E⁵/B D⁵/A E⁵/B   E⁵/B D⁵/A E⁵/B

ALL RIGHT NOW

Words and Music by
Paul Rodgers & Andy Fraser

Full performance demo: CD 1, track 2
Backing only: CD 2, track 2

All right now,— ba - by it's - a all right___ now,_____ woh._____

1.

D.S. al Coda

Let me tell you now. (Mm   eh)

2. I took her

2.

N.C.(A)   (G)   (D)   (A)   (G)   (D)

Play 7 times

Guitar Solo (A)   (G)   (D)   (A)   (G)   (D)

(A)   (G)   (D)   (A)   (G)   (D)

Outro Chorus

I said don't you know. Oh, yeah. All right now,— ba - by it's - a all right— now,—

Repeat ad lib. to fade

— yeah. All right now,— ba - by it's - a all right— now.—

BROWN EYED GIRL

Words and Music by
Van Morrison

Full performance demo: CD 1, track 3
Backing only: CD 2, track 3

Interlude (Bass Solo)

Verse

16

FOR WHOM THE BELL TOLLS

Words and Music by
James Hetfield, Lars Ulrich & Cliff Burton

Full performance demo: CD 1, track 4
Backing only: CD 2, track 4

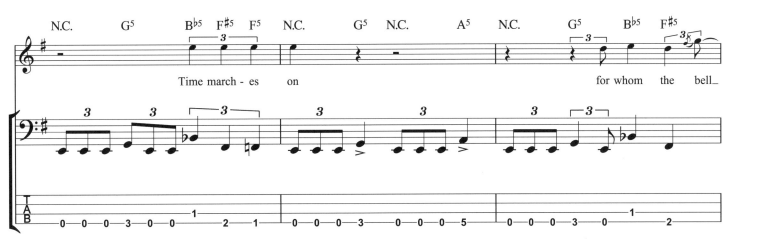

Time march - es   on   for whom   the   bell

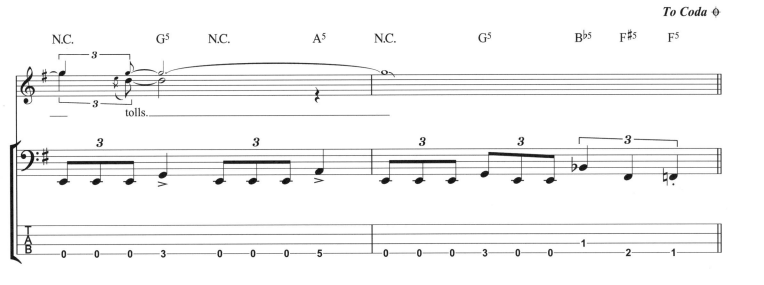

To Coda ⊕

tolls. _____

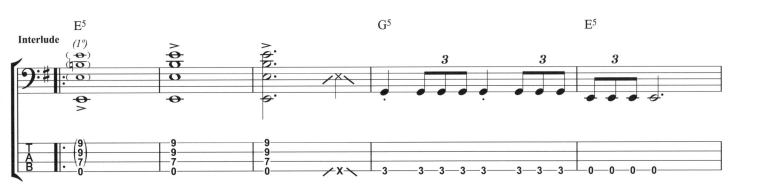

Interlude

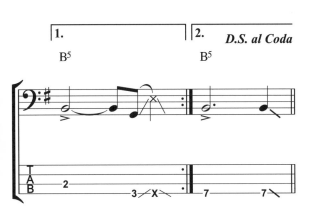

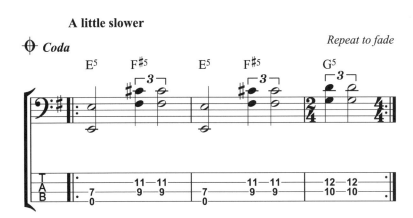

A little slower

Repeat to fade

⊕ *Coda*

1.

2.   *D.S. al Coda*

HEY JOE

Words and Music by
Billy Roberts

Full performance demo: CD 1, track 5
Backing only: CD 2, track 5

26

I SHOT THE SHERIFF

Words and Music by
Bob Marley

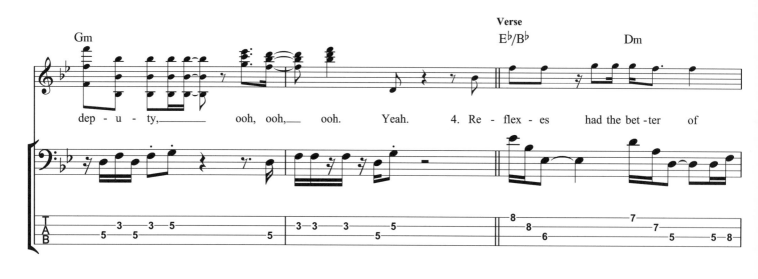

dep - u - ty,_____ ooh, ooh,_____ ooh. Yeah. 4. Re - flex - es had the bet - ter of

me_____ and what is to be will_ be. Ev - 'ry

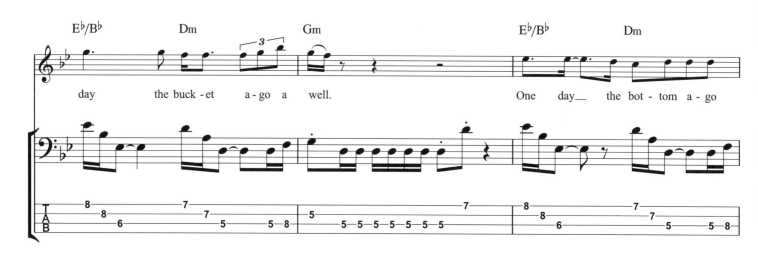

day the buck - et a - go a well. One day_ the bot - tom a - go

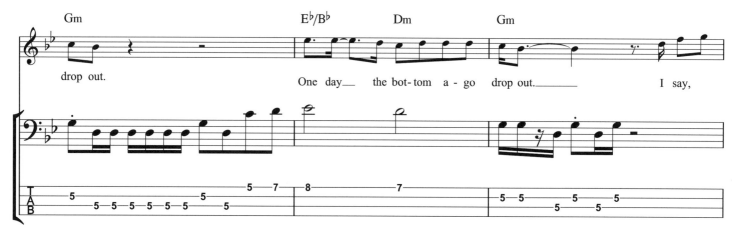

drop out. One day_ the bot - tom a - go drop out._____ I say,

N.C.

Outro Chorus

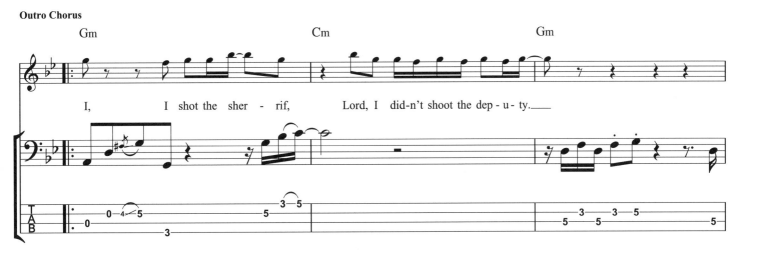

I, I shot the sher - rif, Lord, I did-n't shoot the dep - u - ty.___

I, I, but I did-n't shoot no

repeat w/ad lib. vocals to fade

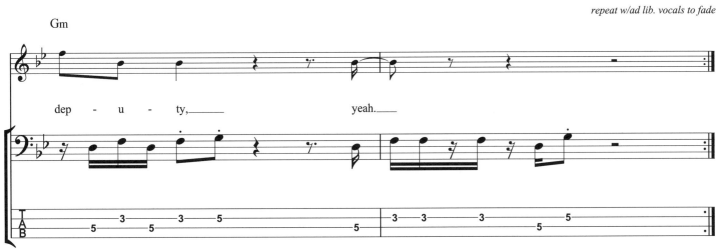

dep - u - ty,___ yeah.___

LADY MADONNA

Words and Music by
John Lennon & Paul McCartney

Full performance demo: CD 1, track 7
Backing only: CD 2, track 7

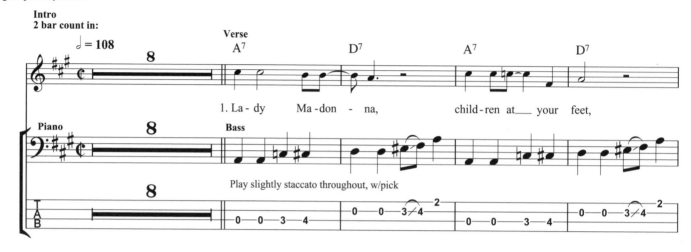

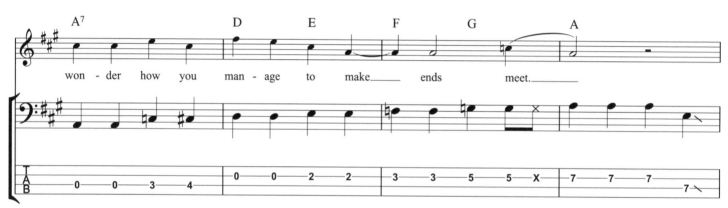

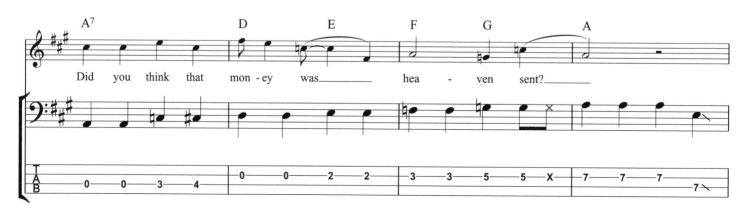

Bridge

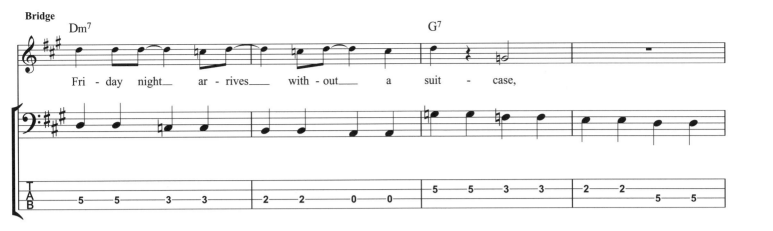

Fri - day night__ ar - rives__ with - out__ a suit - case,

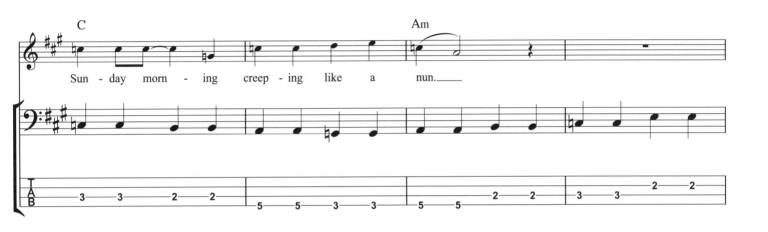

Sun - day morn - ing creep - ing like a nun.__

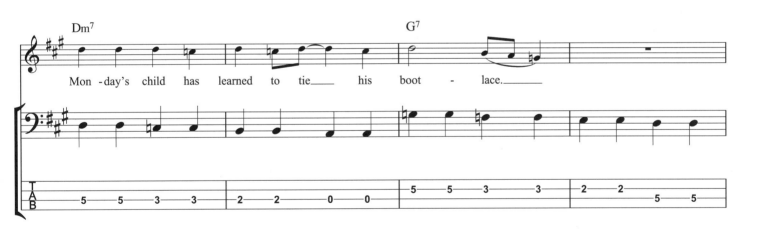

Mon - day's child has learned to tie__ his boot - lace.__

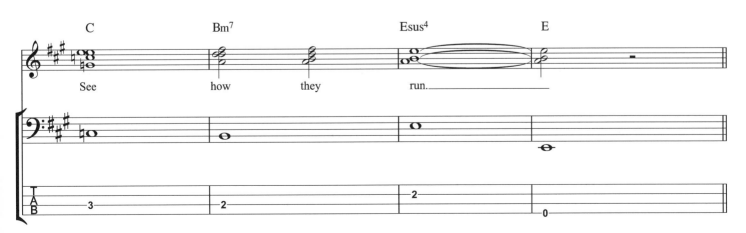

See how they run.__

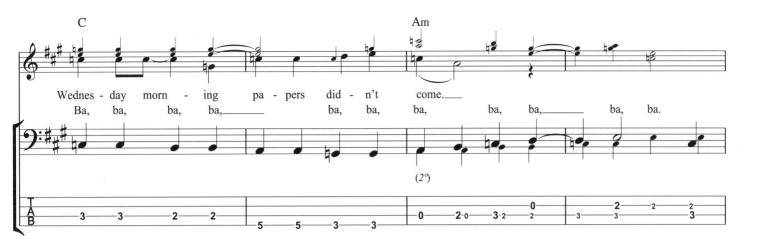

Wednes - day morn - ing pa - pers did - n't come.___
Ba, ba, ba, ba,___ ba, ba, ba, ba, ba,___ ba, ba.

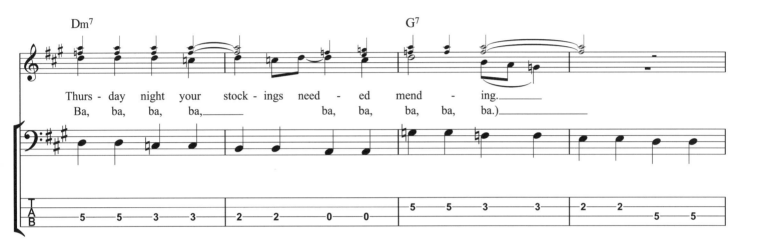

Thurs - day night your stock - ings need - ed mend - ing.___
Ba, ba, ba, ba,___ ba, ba, ba, ba, ba.)___

To Coda

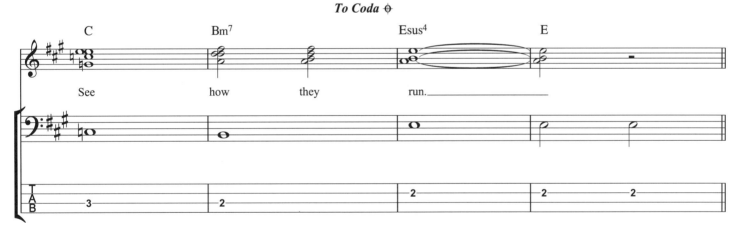

See how they run.___

Verse

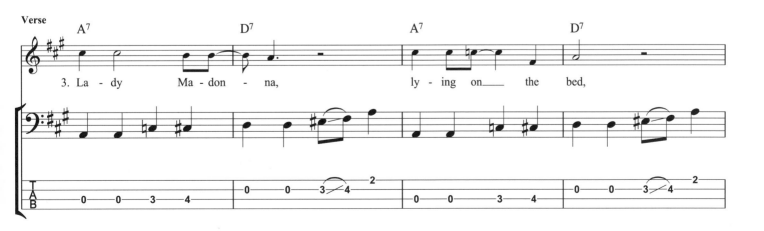

3. La - dy Ma - don - na, ly - ing on___ the bed,

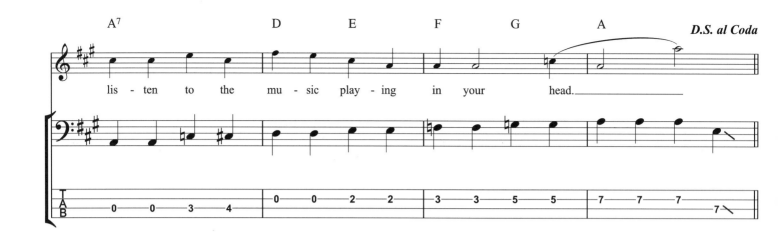

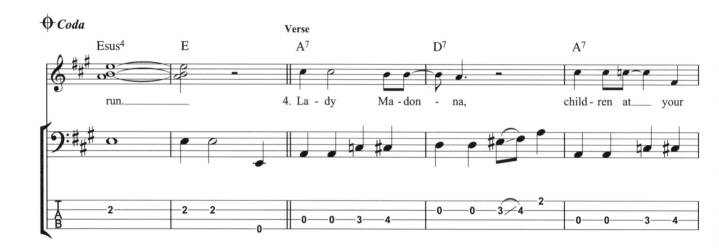

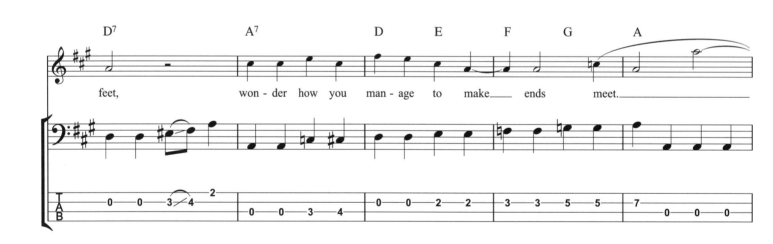

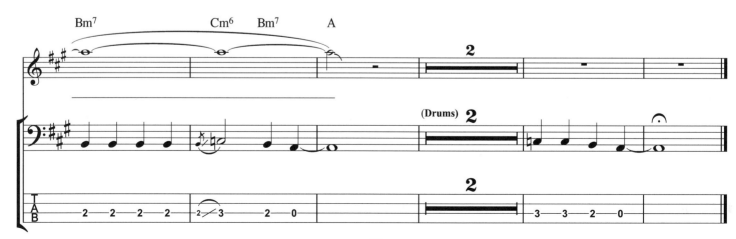

LIVIN' ON A PRAYER

Words and Music by
Jon Bon Jovi, Richie Sambora & Desmond Child

Full performance demo: CD 1, track 8
Backing only: CD 2, track 8

Intro
2 bar count in:

♩ = 122

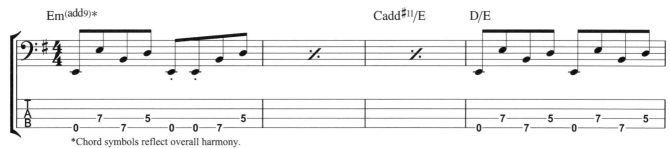

*Chord symbols reflect overall harmony.

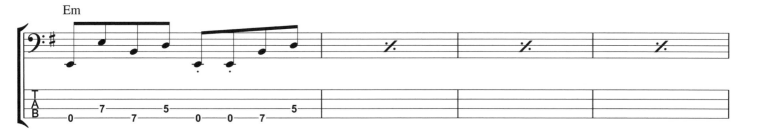

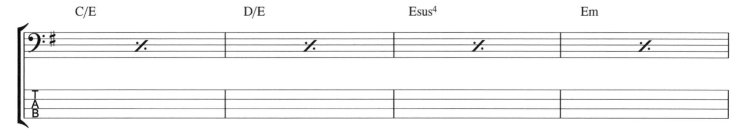

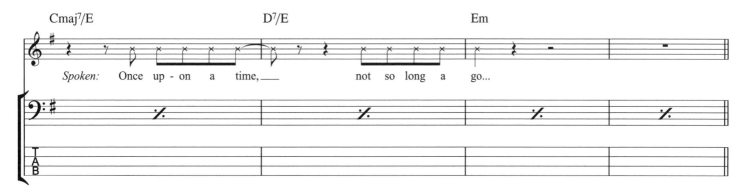

Spoken: Once up-on a time,___ not so long a go...

Verse

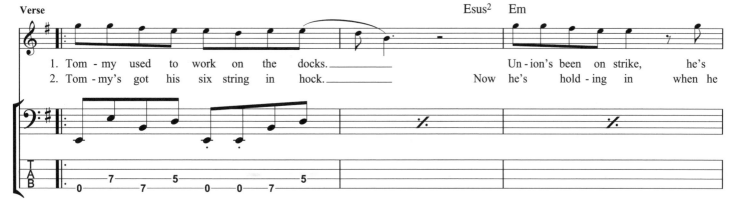

1. Tom-my used to work on the docks.___ Un-ion's been on strike, he's
2. Tom-my's got his six string in hock.___ Now he's hold-ing in when he

down on his luck, it's tough,_____ so tough._____
used to make it talk so tough,_____ mmm, it's tough._____

Gi - na works the din - er all day._____ When she
Gi - na dreams of run - ning a - way._____

Work - ing for her man, she brings home her pay for love,_____
cries in the night, Tom - my whis - pers; "Ba - by, it's o - kay,_____

mmm, for love. _____ She says: We've got to
some - day." _____ We've got to

Pre-Chorus

hold_____ on_____ to what we've got. It does - n't make a dif - f'rence if we

40

Outro-Chorus

LATE IN THE EVENING

Words and Music by
Paul Simon

Full performance demo: CD 1, track 9
Backing only: CD 2, track 9

Intro
4 bar count in:

45

46

4. The

Verse

first thing I___ re - mem - ber, when_ you came___ in - to my life,___ I said "I'm gon-na

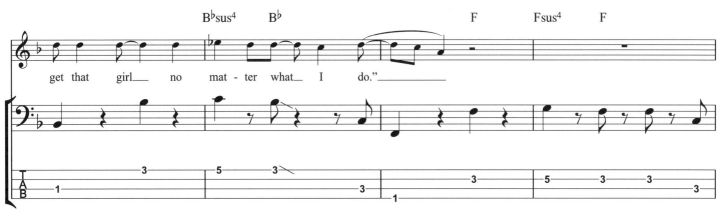

get that girl___ no mat - ter what___ I do."_____

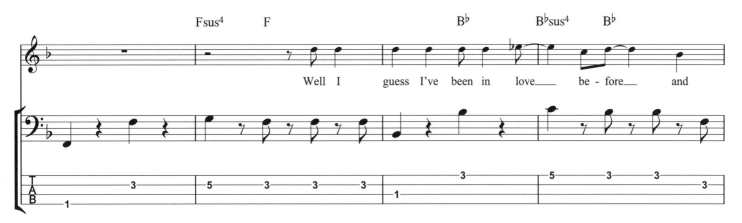

Well I guess I've been in love___ be - fore___ and

LONDON CALLING

Words and Music by
Joe Strummer, Mick Jones, Paul Simonon & Topper Headon

Full performance demo: CD 1, track 10
Backing only: CD 2, track 10

Intro
2 bar count in:

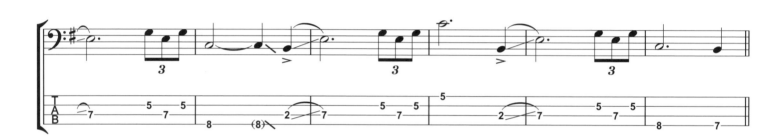

Verse

1. Lon - don call - ing to the far a - way towns._ Now war is de-clared and
2. Lon - don call - ing to the i - mi - ta - tion zone. For - get it, bro -ther, you can

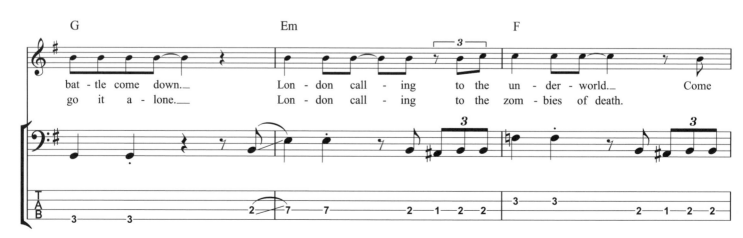

bat - tle come down._ Lon - don call - ing to the un - der - world._ Come
go it a - lone._ Lon - don call - ing to the zom - bies of death.

Chorus

53

wheat is___ grow-ing thin. En-gines stop run-ning but I have no fear 'cause
wheat is___ grow-ing thin. A nu-cle - ar er - ror but I have no fear 'cause

To Coda ⊕

Lon-don is drown-ing and I   live by the riv - er.

D.S. al Coda

The

MY GENERATION

Words and Music by
Pete Townshend

Full performance demo: CD 1, track 11
Backing only: CD 2, track 11

58

Guitar Solo

Outro   w/vocal *ad lib.*

Talk - in' 'bout my gen - er - a - tion.

Talk - in' 'bout my gen - er - a - tion.   Talk - in' 'bout my gen - er - a - tion.

Play 4 times

Talk - in' 'bout my gen - er - a - tion.   Talk - in' 'bout my gen - er - a - tion.

REBEL REBEL

Words and Music by
David Bowie

Full performance demo: CD 1, track 12
Backing only: CD 2, track 12

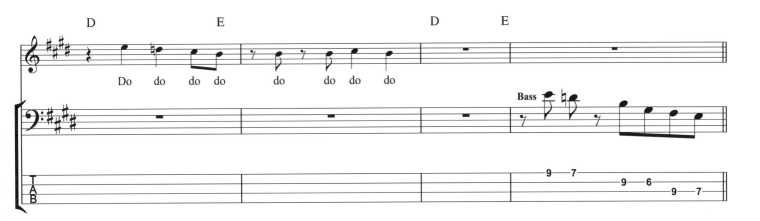

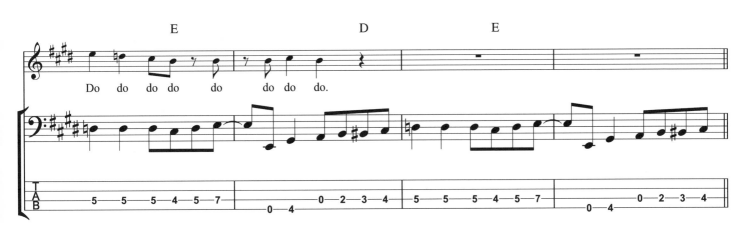

61

Verse

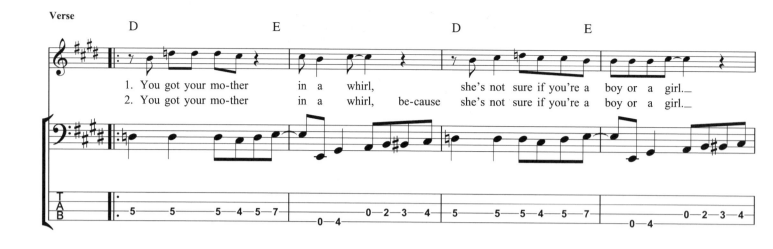

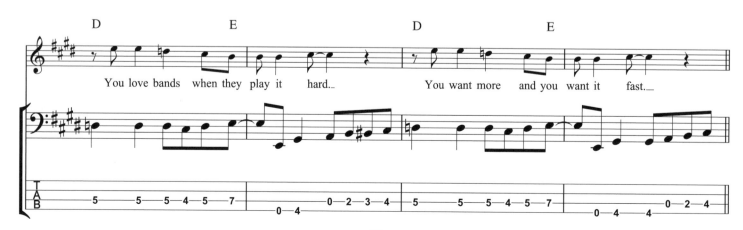

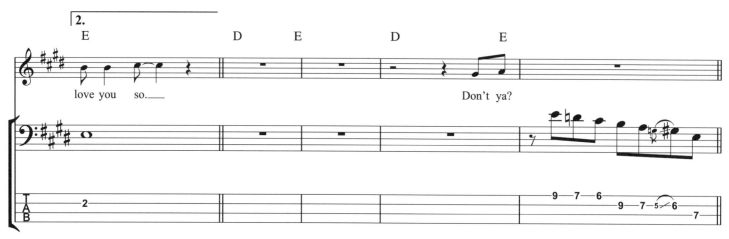

Chorus

64

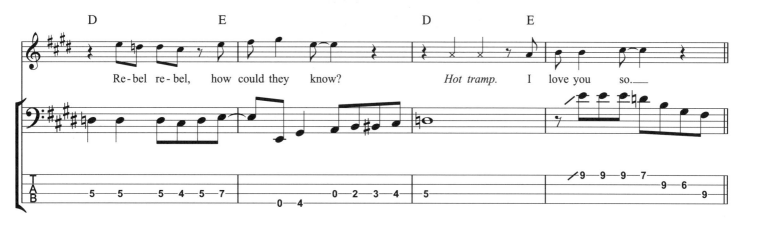

Re-bel re-bel, how could they know? *Hot tramp.* I love you so.___

1. You've

Outro

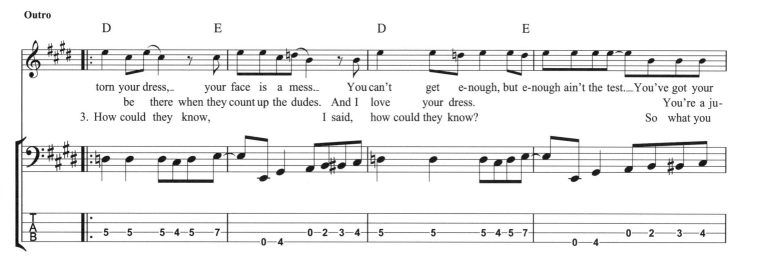

torn your dress,___ your face is a mess.__ You can't get e-nough, but e-nough ain't the test.__You've got your

be there when they count up the dudes. And I love your dress. You're a ju-

3. How could they know, I said, how could they know? So what you

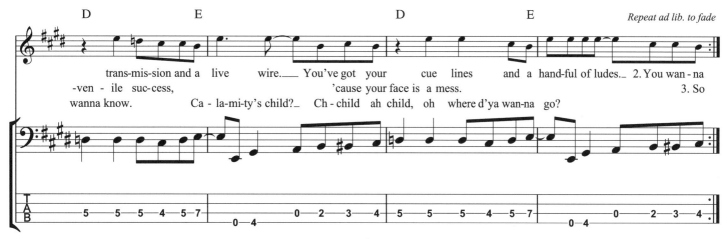

trans-mis-sion and a live wire.__ You've got your cue lines and a hand-ful of ludes._ 2.You wan-na

-ven - ile suc-cess, 'cause your face is a mess. 3. So

wanna know. Ca - la-mi-ty's child?_ Ch - child ah child, oh where d'ya wan-na go?

Repeat ad lib. to fade

MY SHARONA

Words and Music by
Douglas Fieger & Berton Averre

Full performance demo: CD 1, track 13
Backing only: CD 2, track 13

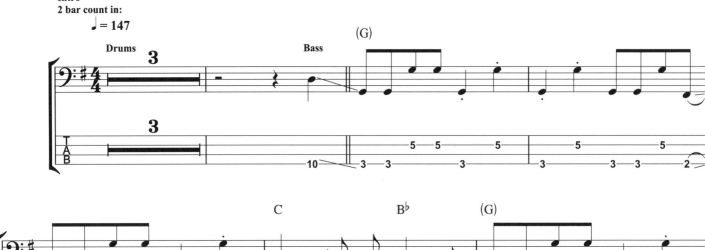

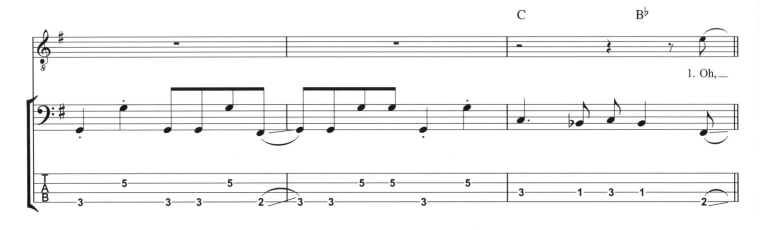

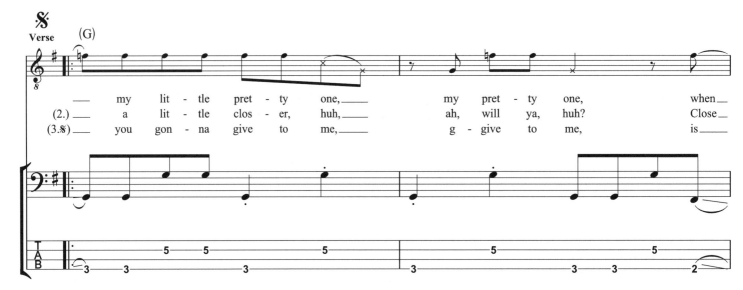

Chorus

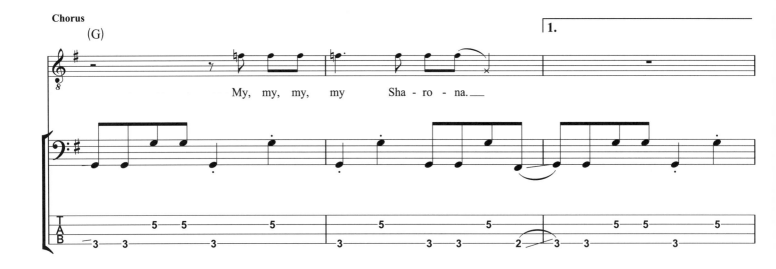

My, my, my, my Sha - ro - na.

2. Come ___ My, my, my, my Sha - ro - na.

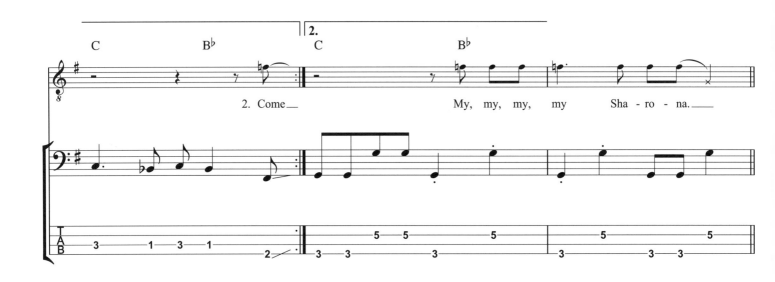

Gtr. Solo

Play 3 times

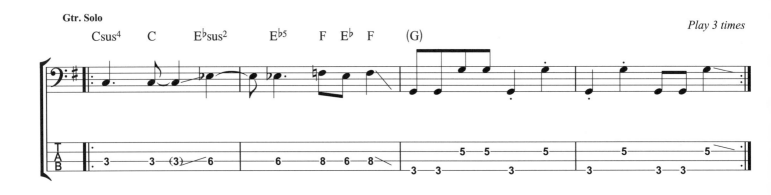

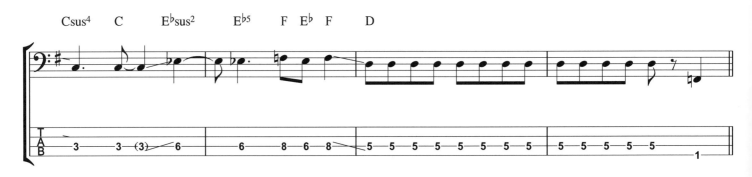

Gtr. Solo

ROPE

Words and Music by
Dave Grohl, Taylor Hawkins, Nate Mendel, Chris Shiflett & Pat Ruthensmear

Full performance demo: CD 1, track 14
Backing only: CD 2, track 14

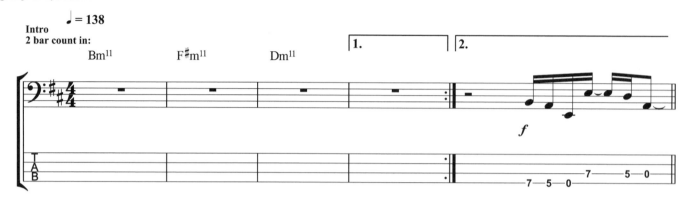

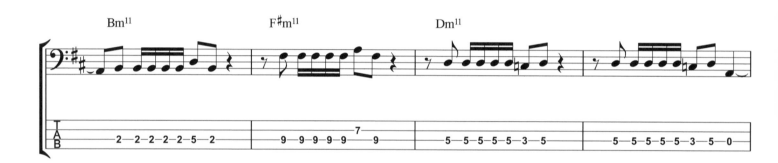

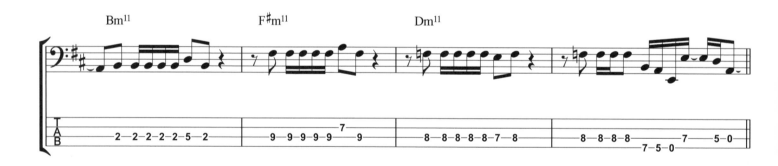

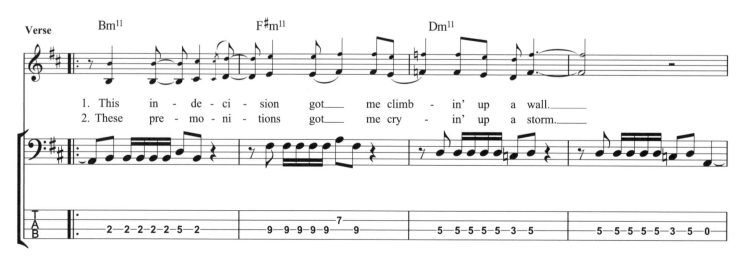

1. This in-de-ci-sion got___ me climb-in' up a wall.___
2. These pre-mo-ni-tions got___ me cry-in' up a storm.___

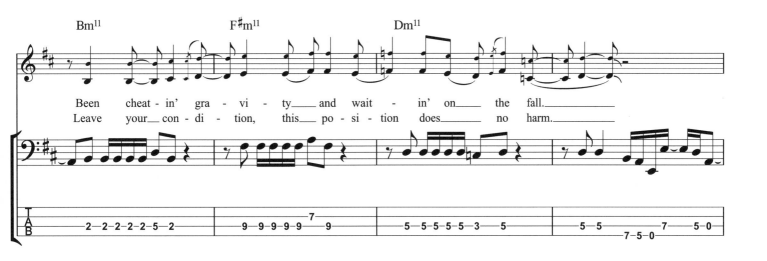

Been cheat-in' gra-vi-ty___ and wait-in' on___ the fall.___
Leave your con-di-tion, this po-si-tion does___ no harm.___

1° only

How did this___ come o-ver me? Thought I was a-bove___ it all.___

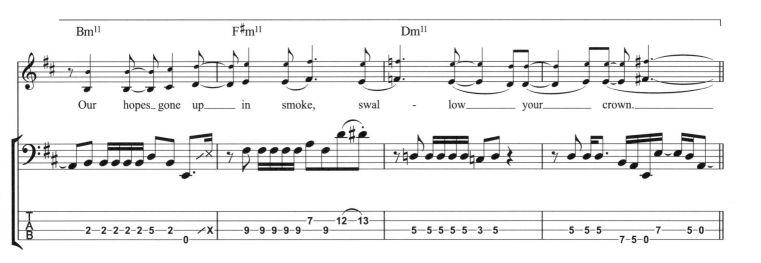

Our hopes__ gone up___ in smoke, swal-low___ your___ crown.___

Pre-chorus

Yow!___ On a___ kiss, thought I'd save___ my breath___ for you.___

73

Bm¹¹　　Bm⁷ Bm¹¹　　F♯m¹¹　　　　Dm¹¹　　Dsus⁴ Dm¹¹　　Dm¹¹　N.C.

Yow!___ On a___ kiss, thought I'd save___ my breath for you.__

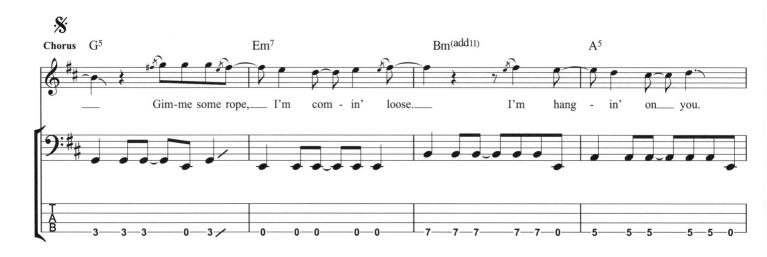

Chorus G⁵　　　　　Em⁷　　　　　Bm⁽ᵃᵈᵈ¹¹⁾　　　A⁵

Gim-me some rope,___ I'm com - in' loose.___ I'm hang - in' on___ you.

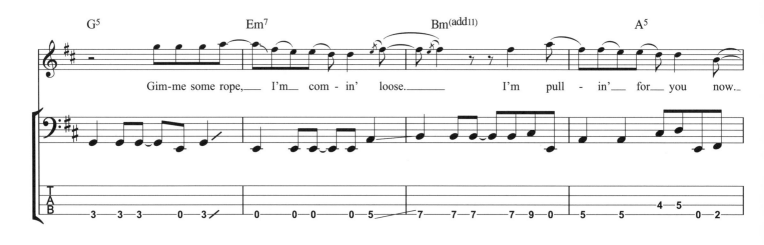

G⁵　　　　　Em⁷　　　　　Bm⁽ᵃᵈᵈ¹¹⁾　　　A⁵

Gim-me some rope,___ I'm___ com - in' loose.___ I'm pull - in'___ for___ you now.__

3° only

To Coda ⊕

G⁵　　　　　Em⁷　　　　　Bm⁽ᵃᵈᵈ¹¹⁾　　　A⁵

Gim-me some hope,___ I'm___ com - in' through.___ I'm count - in'___ on___ you.

Guitar solo

D.S. al Coda

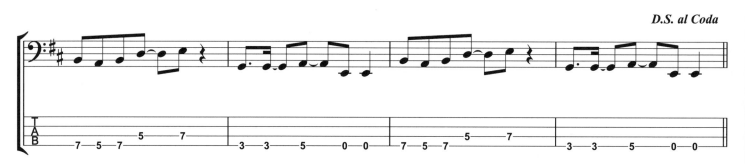

Gim-me some rope,___ I'm com - in' out of my head,___ in - to the clear.__ When

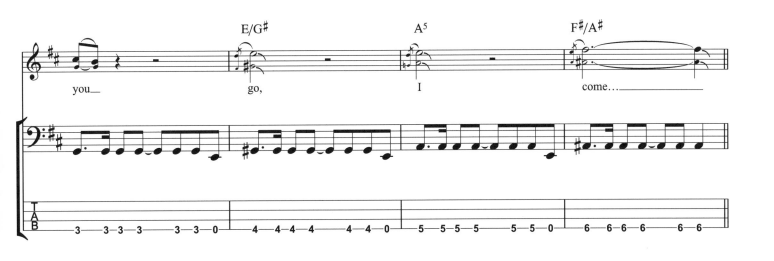

you___ go, I come...___

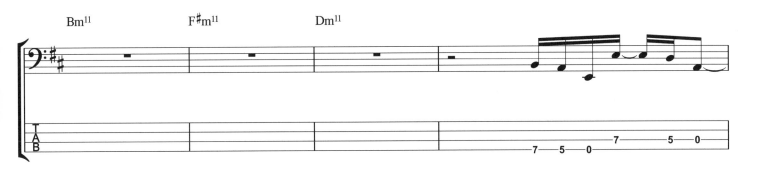

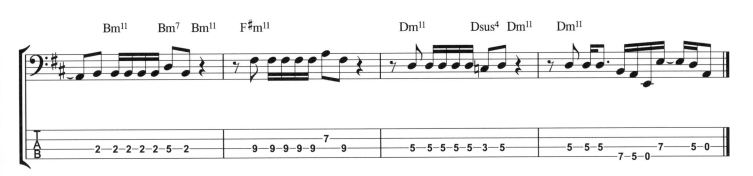

77

ROXANNE

Words and Music by
Sting

Full performance demo: CD 1, track 15
Backing only: CD 2, track 15

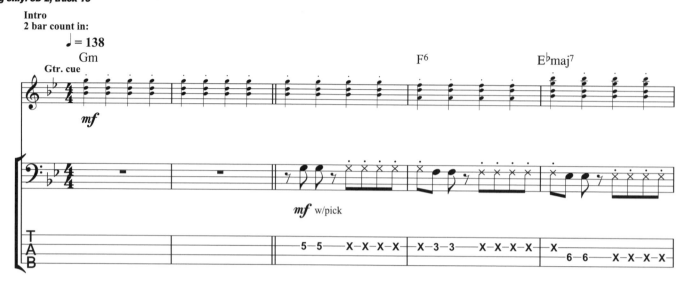

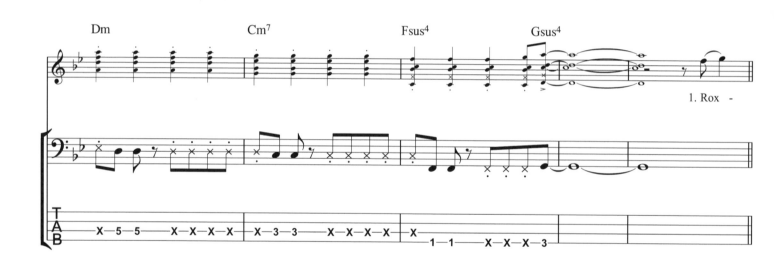

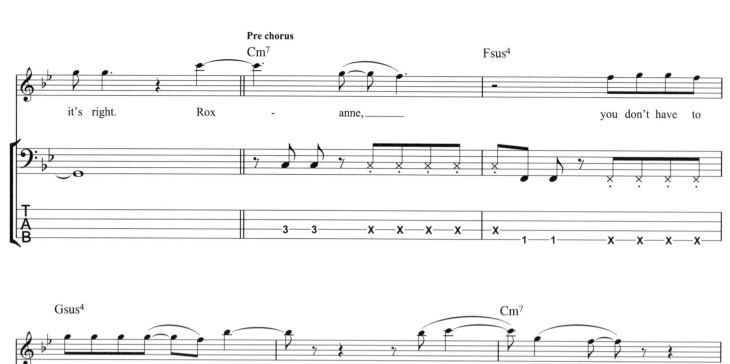

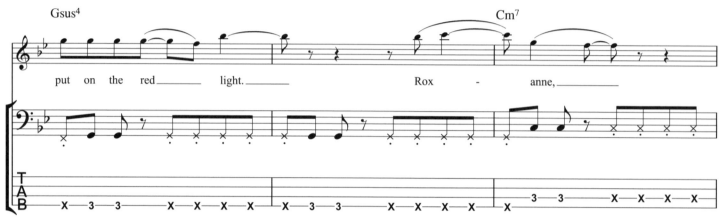

SWEET HOME ALABAMA

Words and Music by
Ronnie Van Zant, Ed King & Gary Rossington

Full performance demo: CD 1, track 16
Backing only: CD 2, track 16

Intro
2 bar count in:
 = 100

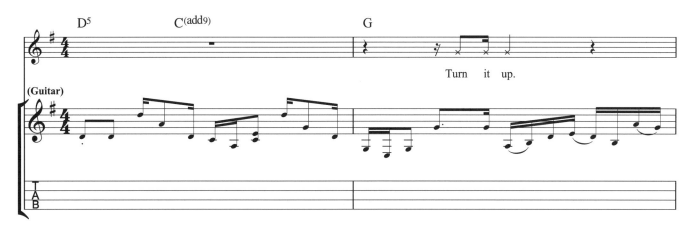

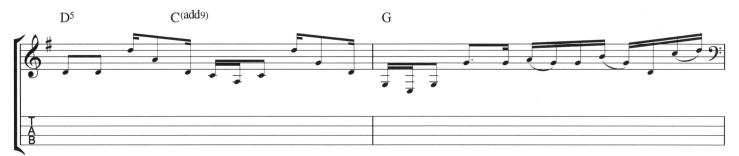

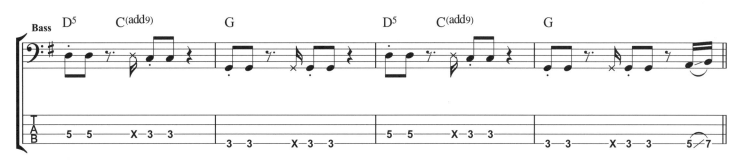

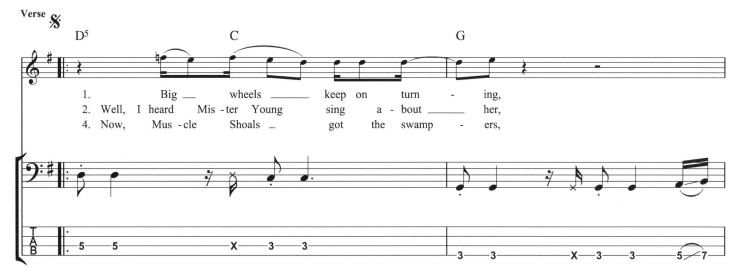

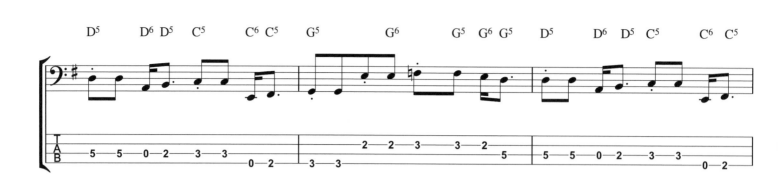

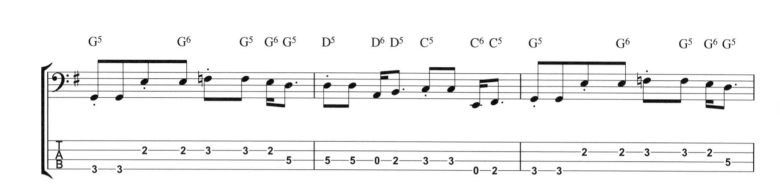

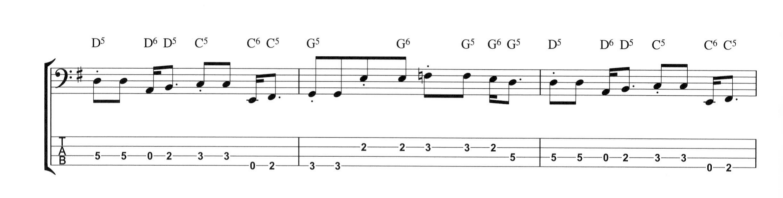

Interlude

D.S. al Coda

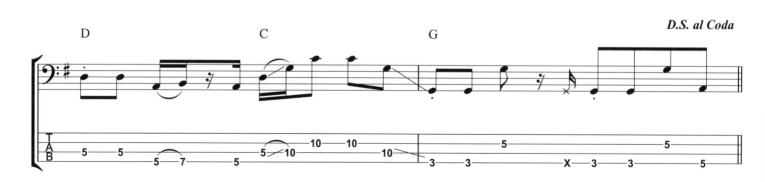

UNDERGROUND

Words and Music by
Ben Folds

Full performance demo: CD 1, track 17
Backing only: CD 2, track 17

VOULEZ-VOUS

Words and Music by
Benny Andersson & Björn Ulvaeus

Full performance demo: CD 1, track 18
Backing only: CD 2, track 18

noth -ing prom -ised, no re - grets._____ Vou - lez - vous?

Ain't__ no big de - ci - sion, you__ know what to do,_____ la ques -tion, c'est vou -lez -

-vous? Vou - lez - vous?_____

And here we

✠ Coda

Vou -lez - vous? A - ha, a-

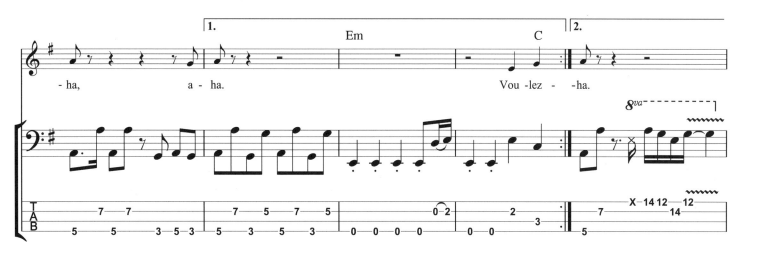

- ha, a - ha. Vou -lez - -ha. Vou -lez -

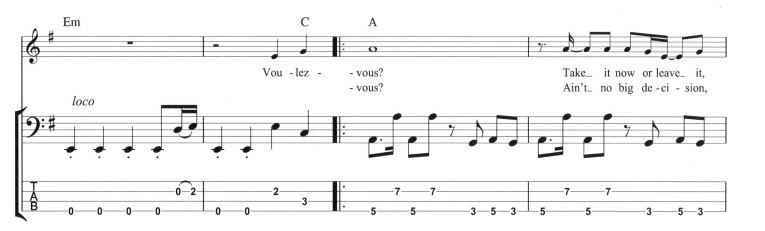

Vou -lez - -vous?
- vous?

Take_ it now or leave_ it,
Ain't_ no big de -ci - sion,

now_ is all we get,____ noth -ing prom -ised, no re - grets._____ Vou - lez -
you_ know what to do,____ la ques -tion, c'est vou -lez - vous?_____ Vou - lez -

Repeat to fade

WONDERWALL

Words and Music by
Noel Gallagher

Full performance demo: CD 1, track 19
Backing only: CD 2, track 19

Intro
2 bar count in:

♩ = 88

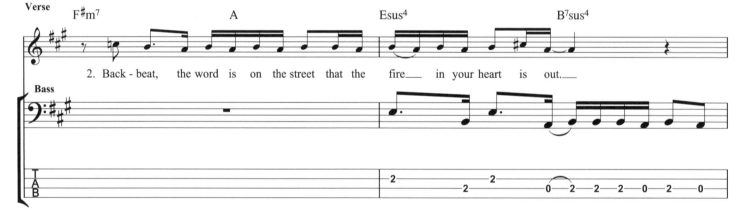

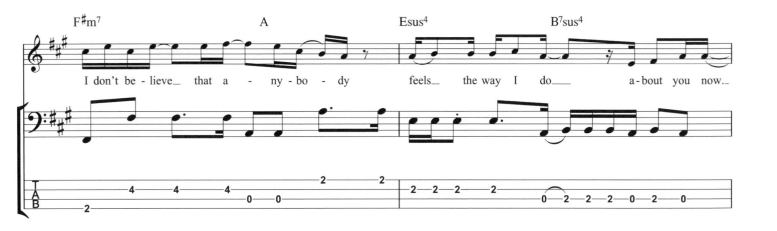

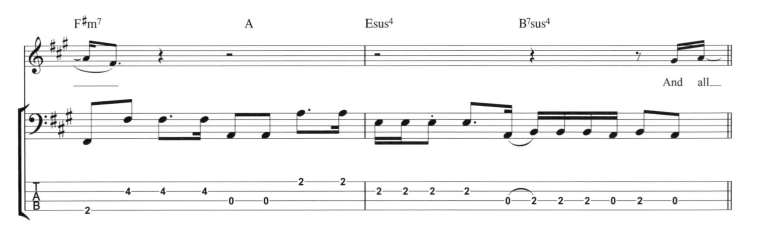

Pre-chorus

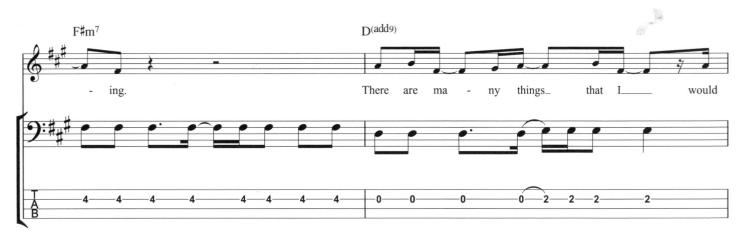

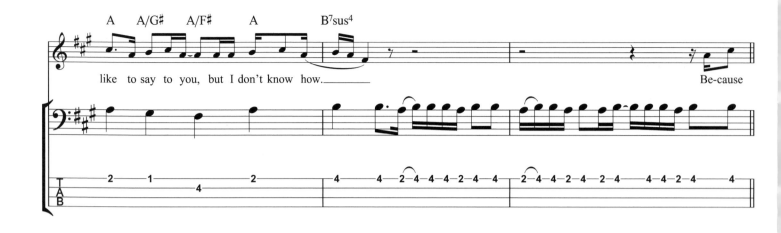

like to say to you, but I don't know how._____ Be-cause

may - be,_____ you're gon - na be the one that saves me?_____

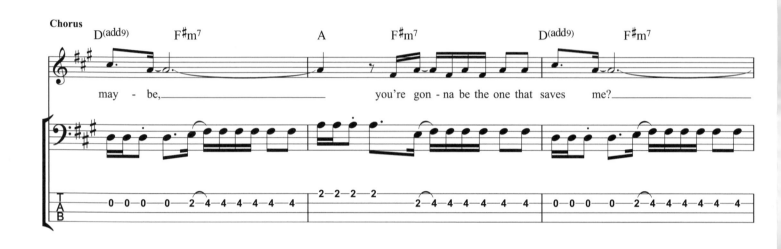

____ And af - ter all,_____ you're my won - der - wall._____

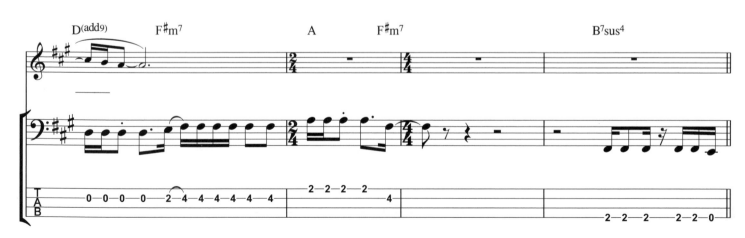

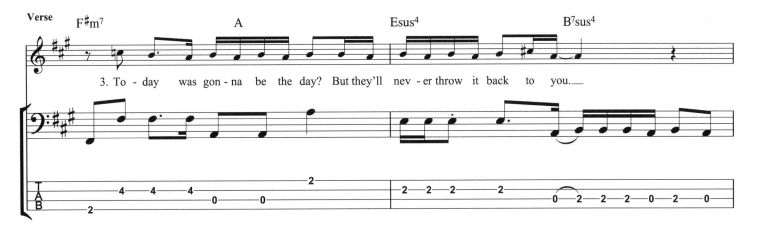

Verse

3. To - day was gon - na be the day? But they'll nev - er throw it back to you.___

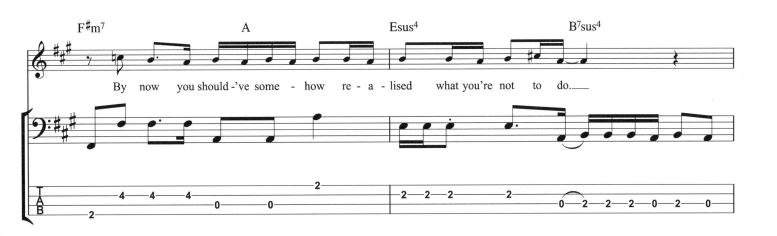

By now you should -'ve some - how re - a - lised what you're not to do.___

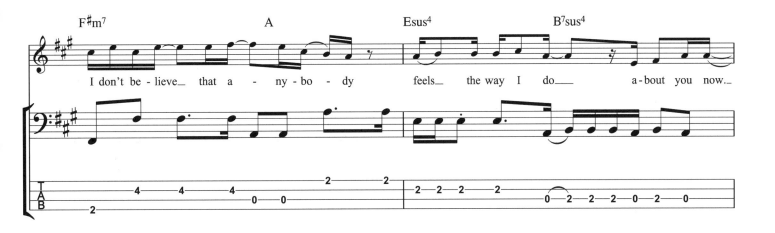

I don't be - lieve___ that a - ny - bo - dy feels___ the way I do___ a - bout you now.___

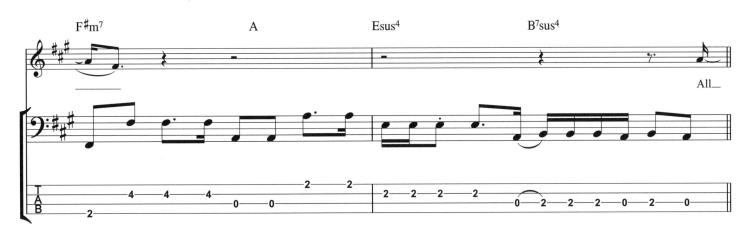

All___

Pre-chorus

D(add9)   Esus⁴   F#m⁷   D(add9)   Esus⁴

__ the roads that lead_ you there are wind - ing,   and all__ the lights that light   the way_ are blind-

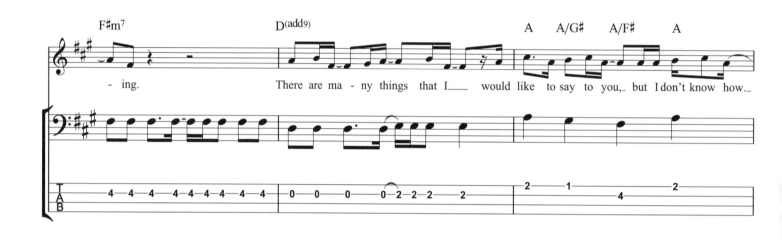

F#m⁷   D(add9)   A   A/G#   A/F#   A

- ing.   There are ma - ny things that I__ would like to say to you,_ but I don't know how.__

B⁷sus⁴

I said

Chorus

D(add9)   F#m⁷   A   F#m⁷   D(add9)   F#m⁷

may - be,_____ you're gon - na be the one that saves   me?_

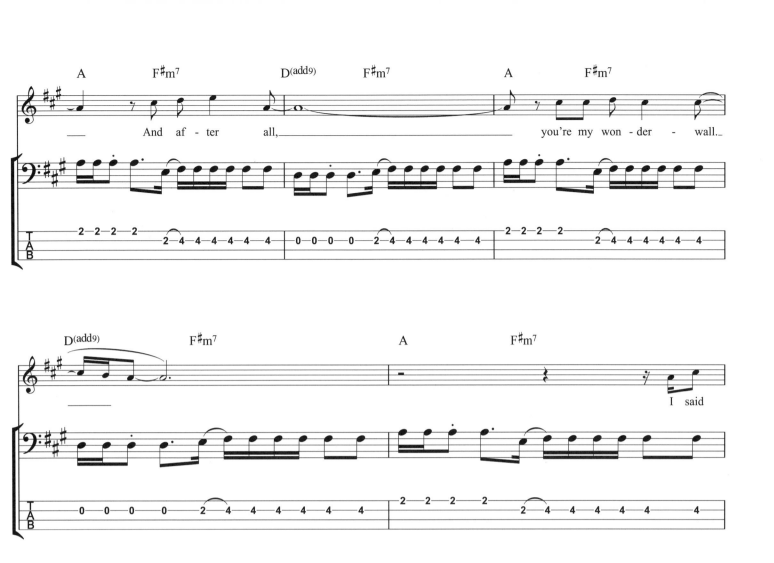

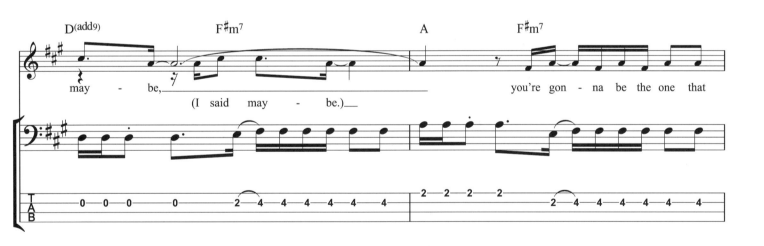

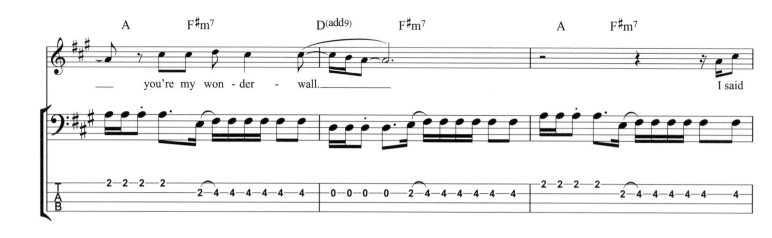

you're my won - der - wall._____ I said

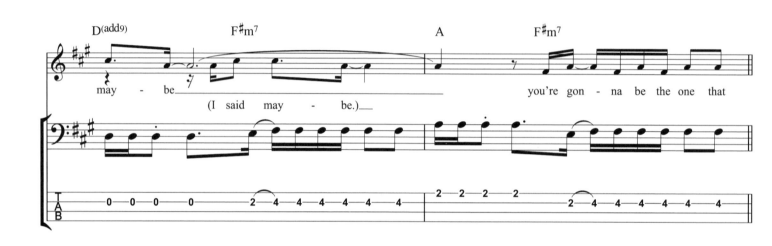

may - be_____
(I said may - be.)_____ you're gon - na be the one that

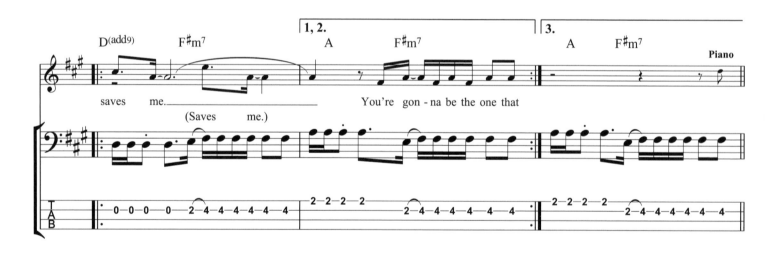

saves me._____
(Saves me.) You're gon - na be the one that

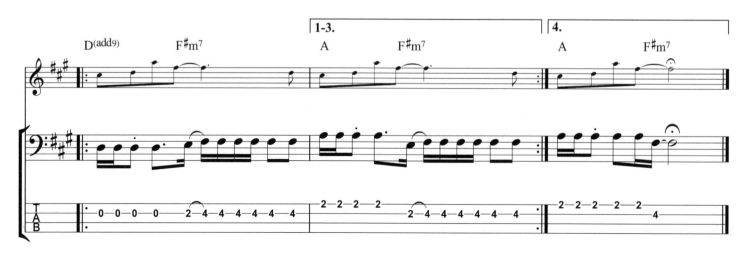

YOU SHOOK ME ALL NIGHT LONG

Words and Music by
Angus Young, Malcolm Young & Brian Johnson

Full performance demo: CD 1, track 20
Backing only: CD 2, track 20

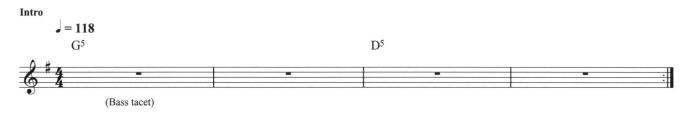

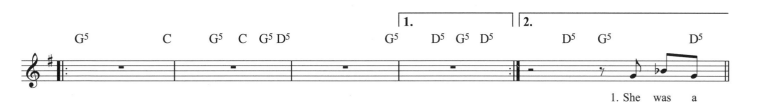

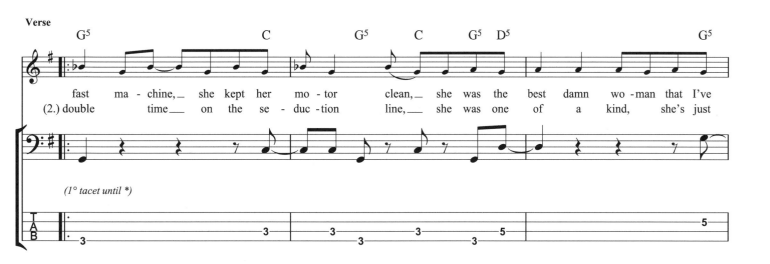

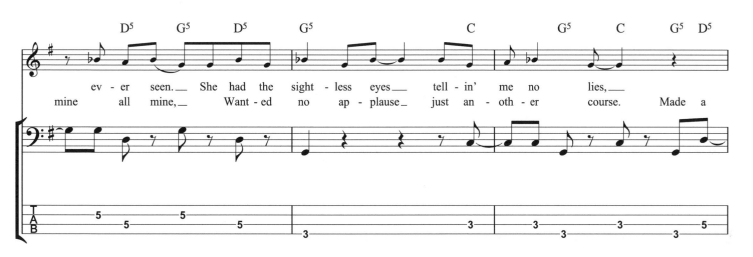

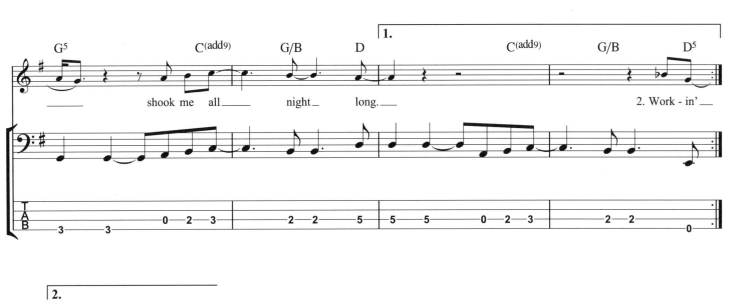

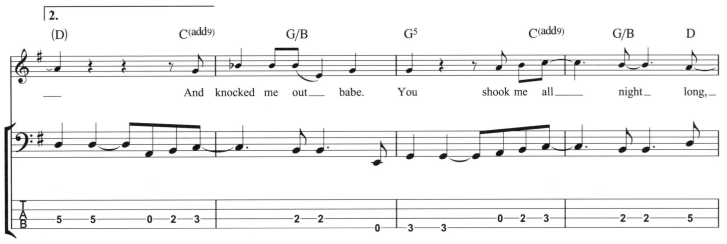

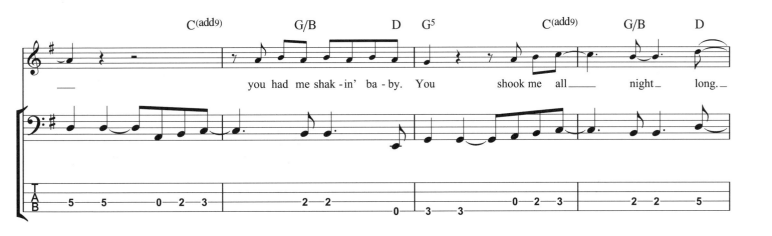

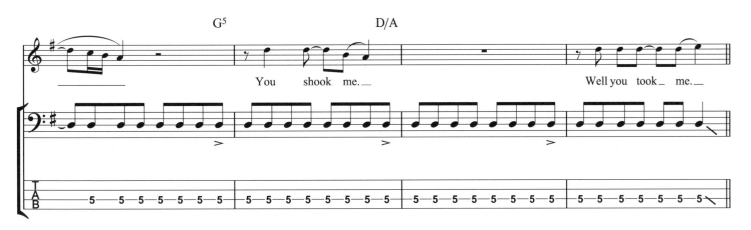

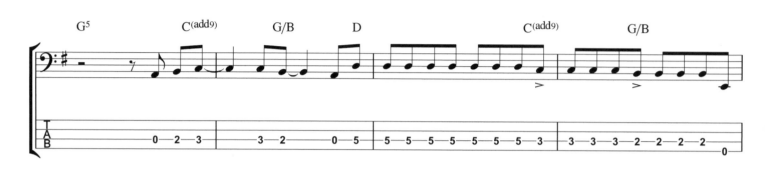

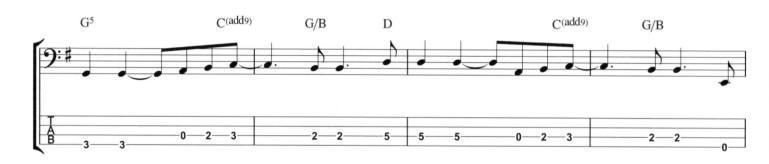

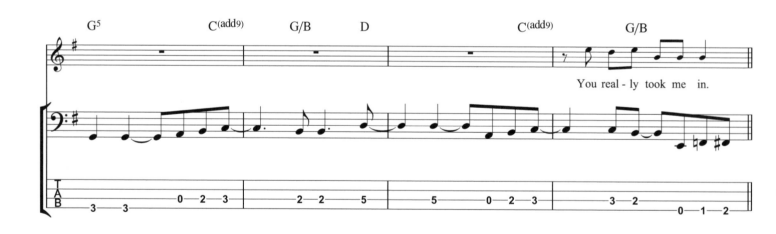

You real - ly took me in.

Chorus

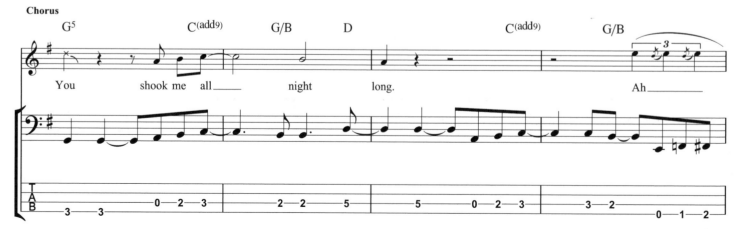

You shook me all____ night long. Ah____

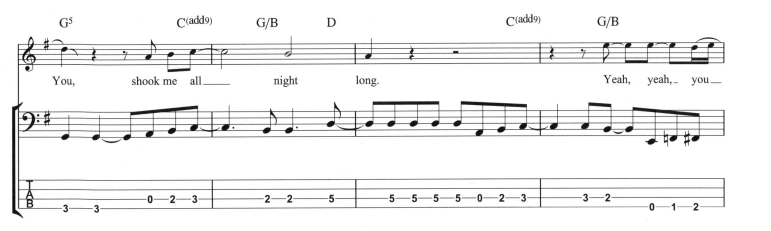

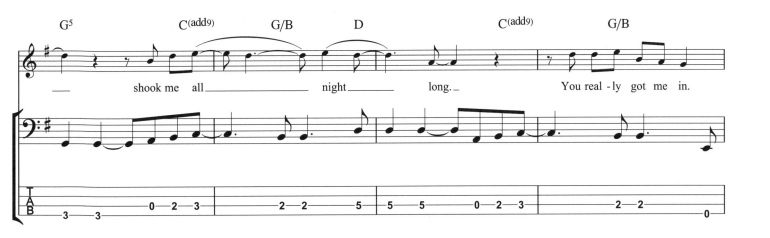

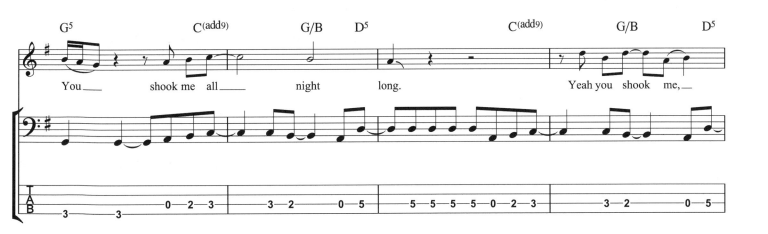

2 3 4 5 6 7 8 9

CD TRACK LISTING

DISC 1
FULL INSTRUMENTAL PERFORMANCES (WITH BASS GUITAR)...

1. **ACE OF SPADES**
(KILMISTER/CLARKE/TAYLOR) MOTOR MUSIC LIMITED

2. **ALL RIGHT NOW**
(RODGERS/FRASER) BLUE MOUNTAIN MUSIC LIMITED

3. **BROWN EYED GIRL**
(MORRISON) UNIVERSAL MUSIC PUBLISHING LIMITED

4. **FOR WHOM THE BELL TOLLS**
(HETFIELD/ULRICH/BURTON) UNIVERSAL MUSIC PUBLISHING LIMITED

5. **HEY JOE**
(ROBERTS) CARLIN MUSIC CORPORATION

6. **I SHOT THE SHERIFF**
(MARLEY) BLUE MOUNTAIN MUSIC LIMITED

7. **LADY MADONNA**
(LENNON/McCARTNEY) SONY/ATV MUSIC PUBLISHING (UK) LIMITED

8. **LATE IN THE EVENING**
(SIMON) UNIVERSAL/MCA MUSIC LIMITED

9. **LIVIN' ON A PRAYER**
(JOVI/SAMBORA/CHILD) UNIVERSAL MUSIC PUBLISHING LIMITED/
SONY/ATV MUSIC PUBLISHING (UK) LIMITED

10. **LONDON CALLING**
(STRUMMER/JONES/SIMONON/HEADON)
UNIVERSAL MUSIC PUBLISHING LIMITED

11. **MY GENERATION**
(TOWNSHEND) FABULOUS MUSIC LIMITED

12. **MY SHARONA**
(FIEGER/AVERRE) CAMPBELL CONNELLY & COMPANY LIMITED/
REACH GLOBAL INC

13. **REBEL REBEL**
(BOWIE) RZO MUSIC LTD/EMI MUSIC PUBLISHING LIMITED/
CHRYSALIS MUSIC LIMITED

14. **ROPE**
(GROHL/HAWKINS/MENDEL/SHIFLETT/RUTHENSMEAR)
BUG MUSIC LIMITED/UNIVERSAL/MCA MUSIC LIMITED

15. **ROXANNE**
(STING) GM SUMNER

16. **SWEET HOME ALABAMA**
(VAN ZANT/KING/ROSSINGTON) UNIVERSAL/MCA MUSIC LIMITED

17. **UNDERGROUND**
(FOLDS) SONY/ATV MUSIC PUBLISHING (UK) LIMITED

18. **VOULEZ-VOUS**
(ANDERSSON/ULVAEUS) BOCU (ABBA) MUSIC/BOCU MUSIC LTD

19. **WONDERWALL**
(GALLAGHER) SONY/ATV MUSIC PUBLISHING (UK) LIMITED

20. **YOU SHOOK ME ALL NIGHT LONG**
(YOUNG/YOUNG/JOHNSON) BUCKS MUSIC GROUP LTD

DISC 2
BACKING TRACKS (WITHOUT BASS GUITAR)...

1. **ACE OF SPADES**
2. **ALL RIGHT NOW**
3. **BROWN EYED GIRL**
4. **FOR WHOM THE BELL TOLLS**
5. **HEY JOE**
6. **I SHOT THE SHERIFF**
7. **LADY MADONNA**
8. **LATE IN THE EVENING**
9. **LIVIN' ON A PRAYER**
10. **LONDON CALLING**
11. **MY GENERATION**
12. **MY SHARONA**
13. **REBEL REBEL**
14. **ROPE**
15. **ROXANNE**
16. **SWEET HOME ALABAMA**
17. **UNDERGROUND**
18. **VOULEZ-VOUS**
19. **WONDERWALL**
20. **YOU SHOOK ME ALL NIGHT LONG**

To remove your CDs from the plastic sleeves,
lift the small lip to break the perforation.
Replace the discs after use for convenient storage.